Origins

Jamie and the Chameleon

Carolyn Sloan ✽ Leslie Harrington

"Is it a mini-dragon?" Jamie asked his mum. Jamie's mum worked at the zoo. She looked after the lizards and snakes. One day, she brought a lizard home for Jamie to see.

Jamie thought the chameleon looked a bit dull sitting in his cage. Then suddenly it stuck its tongue out. And out. And out.

"Wow!" said Jamie. "Did you see that tongue? It went out and out and out and … It's as long as … as …"

"It's as long as his body, so he can catch insects to eat," Mum said.

Mum put the chameleon onto the carpet. It moved around, slowly.

"Mum," said Jamie after a while. "He's going red! Is he all right? Look! He's as red as the carpet."

"Ah!" Mum said. "I forgot to tell you the *really* interesting thing about chameleons. They change colour!"

Mum put the chameleon back in his cage. "Keep an eye on him. I am going to sort out his bug box and get him some water."

Jamie watched the chameleon turn grey again. He watched for a few more minutes, but nothing happened.

Jamie thought, "I'll let him out again and see if he can turn blue this time!" He opened the door to the cage. The chameleon lumbered across the table.

He climbed into the fruit bowl. Soon he turned yellow with brown spots.

"You're brilliant!" laughed Jamie. "Now, time to get back in your cage."

Before Jamie could pick him up, the chameleon had moved into some plants. "Where are you? Stop hiding, PLEASE!" Jamie called. But he had lost him.

The chameleon moved on to the bookshelf next.
"No! Come back! I'll never find you in those books!" Jamie moaned.

Ah there you are!

Lost in the

Then the chameleon saw Mum's patchwork quilt. His eyes swivelled. He began to crawl.

"Not Mum's patchwork quilt!" Jamie groaned. "I'll never, ever find you there!"

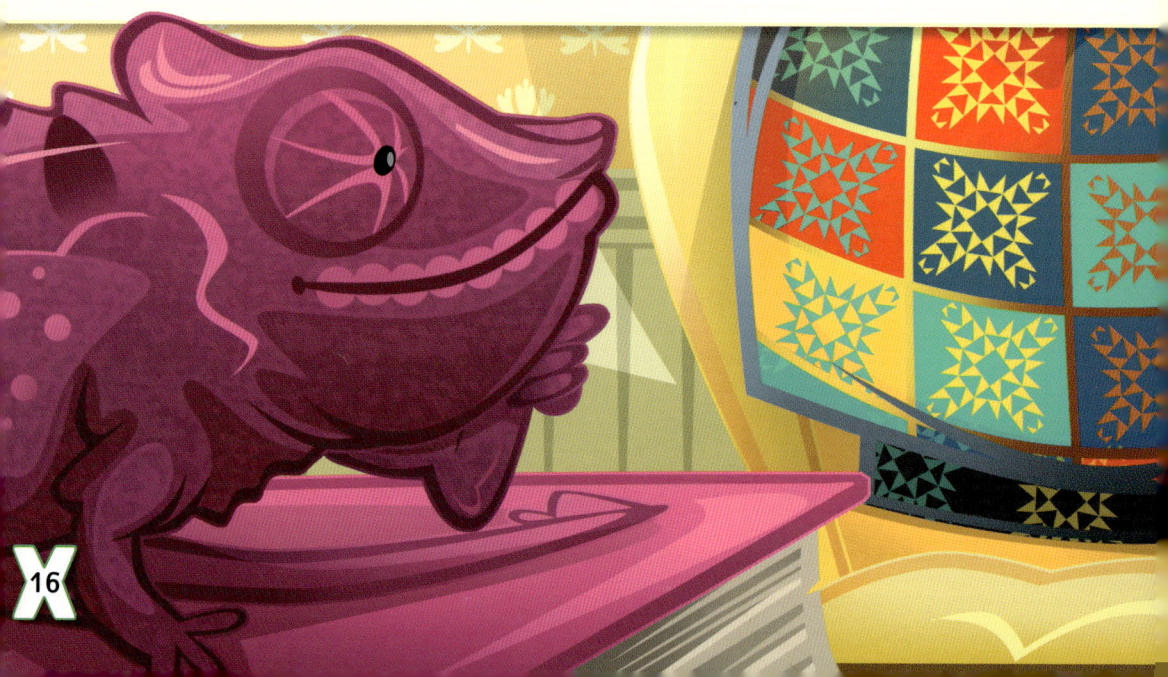

Jamie was scared. The chameleon was changing colour faster than traffic lights. Red, yellow, green. Red, yellow, blue. Then pink, then orange …

"I'm sorry. I let the chameleon out," said Jamie. "He got all muddled on your patchwork quilt and now ... I think he's burst with colours!"

"Don't worry," said Mum, looking around. "He can't have gone far."

"There he is, in his cage," Mum grinned.
Jamie stared. There was the chameleon.
It looked pale and tired – and grey.
But he could see it!

The next day, Mum and Jamie took the chameleon back to the zoo. Jamie was worried that the chameleon might be lonely. "Don't worry, Jamie," Mum said.

"Look how many friends he's got in the chameleon nursery!"

Jamie looked, but all he could see were bushes and plants and … wait! Was that a baby chameleon hiding on a leaf? Was that a bigger one on a flower pot?

"You have to look hard for chameleons!" Jamie said. He started counting them. He counted eight all together. How many can you find?

Chameleons

Chameleons have special colour cells in their skin. Some chameleons can change colour in 20 seconds!

All chameleons have:
- a clasping tail
- eyes that move independently of each other
- a very long tongue

Chameleons change colour for different reasons:
- when they are too hot or too cold
- when they feel moody
- when they want to send a message to other chameleons – like, "Get lost, I'm sleeping!"
- when they feel scared and want to hide.

Why do you think the chameleon in this book changed colour?